The Old Man of Lochnagar

A musical play
based on the book by
H.R.H. The Prince of Wales

Book, music and lyrics by
DAVID WOOD

AMBER LANE PRESS

First published in 1986 by
Amber Lane Press Ltd.
9 Middle Way
Oxford OX2 7LH

Typesetting and make-up by
Oxford Computer Typesetting, Oxford
Printed in Great Britain by Cotswold Press Ltd., Oxford

THE OLD MAN OF LOCHNAGAR, first published by Hamish
Hamilton, London, 1980; issued in paperback by Hamish Hamilton,
1983.

ISBN: 0 906399 78 5

The cover design is based on the Whirligig Theatre poster —
Whirligig Theatre thanks Hamish Hamilton and Sir Hugh Casson for
permission to use an illustration from the original book.

The Old Man of Lochnagar was premièred by Whirligig Theatre at His Majesty's Theatre, Aberdeen in September 1986, followed by a tour including Sadler's Wells Theatre, London, with the following cast:

THE OLD MAN	Iain Lauchlan
GROUSE	Mary-Ann Coburn
GIANT GORMLESS	Percy Copley
NAGAR MAIDS	Lucy Allen
	Katrina Ramsay
LAGOPUS SCOTICUS	Percy Copley
LOCH-HAGGIS	Teresa Gallagher
	Lesley Halliday
	Alec Westwood
SPIDER	Percy Copley
GORMS	Lucy Allen
	Edward Brittain
	Alan Morley
	Katrina Ramsay
QUEEN OF THE GORMS	Mary-Ann Coburn
STAG BEETLE	Lesley Halliday

MUSICAL DIRECTOR/KEYBOARDS
Simon Lee

Director:	David Wood
Designer:	Susie Caulcutt
Choreographer:	Sheila Falconer
Musical Supervisor	Peter Pontzen
Lighting Designer:	Roger Frith
Sound:	Paul Farrah
Puppetry·	Paul Aylett

Produced for Whirligig Theatre by John Gould and David Wood

CHARACTERS

THE OLD MAN		
GROUSE	–	the Old Man's home help — a female bird
GIANT GORMLESS	–	a not especially tall Giant
2 NAGAR MAIDS	–	freshwater Mermaids
LAGOPUS SCOTICUS	–	the King of the Loch
3 LOCH-HAGGIS (a thrace)	–	plump, cheeky, unpredictable
THE PIG EAGLE	–	a large puppet
SPIDER		
GORMS (6 or more)	–	energetic, acrobatic creatures
QUEEN OF THE GORMS	–	their large Sovereign
STAG BEETLE		

Suggested doubling for a cast of 12 actors

M	The Old Man	F	Loch-haggis 2
F	Grouse / Queen of the Gorms	M	Loch-haggis 3
M	Giant Gormless / Lagopus Scoticus / Spider	M	Gorm 3
F	Nagar Maid 1 / Gorm 1	M	Gorm 4
F	Nagar Maid 2 / Gorm 2	M	Gorm 5
F	Loch-haggis 1 / Stag Beetle	F	Gorm 6

ACT ONE

SCENE ONE — The Old Man's Cave

The cave is in the rocks by the loch. Its opening has been covered with deerskin to make a door. A door-knocker is made of a stag's antler attached to the rock so that it is visible when the deerskin is pulled back, as is the water of the loch.

The interior has been made comfortable with a small bed and chair made on rock ledges and boulders. A wood stove, a table, a bookcase and a cupboard have also been successfully improvised, with tartan coverings. Candles and lanterns illuminate the cave. In its own rock recess stands THE OLD MAN's *lavatory. It has an upholstered leather seat, and the flushing mechanism consists of a set of antique bagpipes; when a certain pipe is pulled, the lavatory flushes and a Scottish tune plays at the same time. Other pipes do other things. Rows of books for reading while on the lavatory are conveniently accessible.*

As the Overture finishes, the curtain rises to reveal THE OLD MAN *on the lavatory, reading a large, old tome. He is unaware of the audience. He turns a page.*

After a pause he reaches up and pulls a pipe. The lavatory flushes noisily and gurgily, accompanied by 'Scotland the Brave'.

THE OLD MAN *suddenly looks up and registers* THE AUDIENCE.

OLD MAN: [*with a gasp*] Suffering sporrans! Toss my caber! I've been spotted! Spied upon! And me on the loo, too! [*to* THE AUDIENCE] Peepers shut! Close your eyes!
　　[*He quickly adjusts his dress.*]
How embarrassing! Caught with my knickerbockers down! I expect you're all thinking, 'What a rude old man, what a way to welcome his guests, squatting on

the loo, tha' noo!' Eh? Right. Peepers open. All
decent! Hall-oo!

AUDIENCE: Hall-oo!

OLD MAN: Hall-oo-oo!

AUDIENCE: Hall-oo-oo!

OLD MAN: Welcome ...

Song One: **Welcome to Lochnagar**

Welcome to my lands
The Highlands of Scotland
Wherever you travel
No matter how far
You'll never encounter
A welcome so warm
As your welcome to Lochnagar.

To the east Aberdeen
Inverness to the west
But here in the Highlands
Is the place I love best
Where the lakes are called lochs
And the Johns are called Jocks
Welcome to Lochnagar.

So welcome to my lands
The Highlands of Scotland
Wherever you travel
No matter how far
You'll never encounter
A welcome so warm
As your welcome to Lochnagar.

Living here may appear
At first glance rather odd
But the pros beat the cons
For the cons are all mod.
This pipe here dries my socks
This pipe here winds my clocks
And pull this one, my fav'rite
For Scotch on the rocks.
Where the lakes are called lochs

And the Johns are called Jocks
Welcome to Lochnagar.

So welcome to my lands
The Highlands of Scotland
Wherever you travel
No matter how far
You'll never encounter
A welcome so warm
As your welcome to Lochnagar.

Welcome to each one of you
Welcome to my cave
Welcome to my special loo
That plays 'Scotland the Brave'.

I can do as I please
For I have nae a wife
No, but seriously
'Tis a wonderful life
There are few nasty shocks
On my door no-one knocks
And my friends are the mountain
The trees and the rocks.
This pipe here dries my socks
This pipe here winds my clocks
And pull this one, my fav'rite
For Scotch on the rocks.
Where the lakes are called lochs
And the Johns are called Jocks
Welcome to Lochnagar.

So welcome to my lands
The Highlands of Scotland
Wherever you travel
No matter how far
You'll never encounter
A welcome so warm
As your welcome to Lochnagar.

I've just been reading. I love reading. Especially on
the loo. Best place for a wee bit of peace and quiet.

[*He shows* THE AUDIENCE *his book.*]

The weird and wonderful legends and stories of the Scottish Highlands. Tales of ghosties and beasties, fairies and phantoms, hobgoblins and monsters.

[*Music as* THE OLD MAN *sits down with his book.*]

But I'm sure you don't like stories like that. Eh? Too creepy for you, eh?

[*Hopefully* THE AUDIENCE *denies this.*]

Would you like to hear some?

[*Hopefully* THE AUDIENCE *says 'Yes'.*]

Y'would? Good!

[*The lighting becomes more intimate and spooky. Reflected flames from the stove light* THE OLD MAN'*s face.*]

I could tell you stories about ... the Boobri.

[*He shows a picture.*]

The Boobri is a gigantic bird with a loud, hoarse voice and webbed feet. It comes out of the water and gobbles up sheep and cattle, then disappears again. I could tell you about the fairies, good fairies — and evil fairies who steal children. 'Tis said that here in the Highlands the fairies can sometimes be seen — inside their hills, the tops of which, come the full moon, rise up on pillars. I could tell you stories of the Highland Kelpie ...

[*He shows a picture.*]

... a demon in the shape of a horse. The Kelpie is bloodthirsty and ever-hungry for human life. [*confidentially and atmospherically telling the story*] Once upon a Sunday, seven little girls go out walking by the side of the loch and see a charming little horse. One by one they climb on its back, which stretches and stretches longer and longer to allow them all room to sit. A little boy who is with them doesn't want to mount the horse. So the horse turns its head and suddenly yells, 'Come on, scabby-head, get up too!' The boy runs for his life and hides among the boulders. Then the Kelpie gallops hard into the loch with the seven little girls on its back. And they were never seen again ...

[THE OLD MAN *shudders.*]

But not all the legends are frightening. Not all the creatures are nasty. There's the Ghille Dubh over on the west coast. 'Tis said he dresses in leaves and moss. He looks after lost children and leads them home. And then there are my favourites. The Gorms. The Gorms are happy wee creatures about this high ...

[*He indicates just below knee height.*]

... energetic and athletic. 'Tis said that every year they hold their own Highland Games — or, as they call them, Highland Gorms. They live under the stone cairns on the hillsides — indeed you may have heard of the Cairn Gorms. On the Highlands wild heather grows. White heather, and a special variety of purple heather. 'Tis said this is because in the dead of night the Gorms spray the white heather with their own purple dye, home-brewed from the bristles of thistles. They squirt it down from wee flying machines called heathercraft, to make the heather more attractive for the tourists.

[*He yawns.*]

Wondrous creatures, Gorms. My life's ambition is to meet them.

[*He yawns.*]

Excuse me. But Gorm sightings have been as rare as Loch Ness Monster sightings, so ...

[*He yawns.*]

... perhaps I'll only ever dream of seeing them...

[*He falls asleep. He snores and whistles several times.*]

[*Gradually the lighting brightens as though morning has risen.*]

[*Suddenly the deerskin door is drawn aside and in bustles* GROUSE, *the bird who keeps house for* THE OLD MAN. *She carries a basket of goodies. She registers the sleeping* OLD MAN *with impati-*

ence, then lights the stove. She takes a large cooking pot, goes to fill it from a jar marked 'Heather Porridge', thinks better of it, picks up a wooden spoon, creeps to a position inches from THE OLD MAN's *ear, then bangs the spoon loudly against the cooking pot.*]

[THE OLD MAN *wakes with a jump.*]

OLD MAN: Oh, 'tis you, Grouse.

GROUSE: Aye, 'tis I, Old Man.
[*She returns to the stove and starts preparing heather porridge.*]

OLD MAN: Good morning.

GROUSE: Huh! Little good about *my* morning.
[THE OLD MAN *gets up and goes to the doorway.*]

OLD MAN: The sun shines bright from a clear blue sky. The loch looks calm and still as a mirror.

GROUSE: You'd better go look in it, then. At your reflection. Maybe you'll see the selfish Old Man I see.

OLD MAN: Selfish? Me?

GROUSE: Selfish. You.

OLD MAN: You miserable old bird.

GROUSE: Don't you miserable old bird me, you miserable Old Man. I've been off my nest since dawn flying hither and thither on your behalf. My wings are dropping off.

OLD MAN: Oh, stop grousing, Grousy.

GROUSE: 'Tis all very well for you. Snoring your selfish old head off till I arrive with your breakfast.

OLD MAN: Ah, breakfast!
[*He eagerly sits at the table.*]
You're a jewel, Grousy. A wee gem! A treasure.

GROUSE: You're just saying that.

OLD MAN: Because it's true!

GROUSE: Because you want your breakfast.

OLD MAN: Well, I wouldna say no. What is there?

GROUSE: Heather porridge with fresh clover juice.

OLD MAN: Delicious!

GROUSE: [*producing them from her bag*] Newly picked blaeberries.

OLD MAN: Blaeberries! My favourite fruit!

GROUSE: Three slices of deer bacon.

OLD MAN: Mm! Deer bacon, you dear Grouse!

GROUSE: And ... though why I bother, heaven alone knows ... a ptarmigan's egg.
[*She holds it up.*]

OLD MAN: [*amazed and delighted*] A ptarmigan's egg? A delicacy rare indeed! Grousy, you didn't ...?

GROUSE: I did.

OLD MAN: You flew?

GROUSE: I flew.

OLD MAN: All the way ...

GROUSE: ... up the mountain

OLD MAN: ... to your cousin?

GROUSE: [*nodding*] She laid it special.

OLD MAN: No wonder your wings are tired. Thank you, Grousy, thank you.

GROUSE: You don't deserve it.
[*She fills a kettle of water and puts it on the stove.*]

OLD MAN: I don't, I don't.
[*He offers her his chair.*]
Come and rest. Take the weight off your tail feathers.

GROUSE: Get away! A rest? And who'll cook your egg for you if I rest? [*raising her voice*] Then your bed needs making and your bread needs baking ...

OLD MAN: And my head is aching! Shut your beak, Grousy. Please.

GROUSE: Why don't you take yourself off and away? Eh? For a holiday. *Then* I'd have a rest.

OLD MAN: There's no place like home, Grousy. An old man's cave is his castle. [*changing the subject*] How was your cousin Ptarmigan?

GROUSE: Toffee-beaked as ever. They're all the same, that side of the family. Just because they live higher up than we mere grouse, they act as though they're higher up. All posh and la-di-da.

OLD MAN: She does lay a lovely egg. All I can do is lay the table!

GROUSE: And it's not often you do that. Oh, and I've brought

you something to brighten up your cave. Some
heather.

> [*She produces it and finds a stone vase to put it in.*]

OLD MAN: Grousy, you've excelled yourself. You ... [*sees the heather*] But it's white.

GROUSE: Well?

OLD MAN: You know I prefer purple.

GROUSE: Do you want heather or don't you?

OLD MAN: I want purple heather, you silly old bird!

GROUSE: Then get it yourself, you silly Old Man!

OLD MAN: I will, I will!

> [*He goes to the doorway.*]

GROUSE: You won't, you won't!

OLD MAN: I will!

GROUSE: You won't!

OLD MAN: Why not?

GROUSE: There isn't any.

> [*Dramatic chord.*]

OLD MAN: There isn't any?

GROUSE: Not a clump.

OLD MAN: Not a clump?

GROUSE: Not a sprig.

OLD MAN: Not a sprig?

GROUSE: Not a petal.

OLD MAN: Not a petal? That's impossible.

GROUSE: Impossible, but true ...

Song Two: **Heather Lament**

The heather is white
For miles around
Over I circled for over an hour
But way down below
Sad to say I saw no
Sight of a purple flower.

OLD MAN: Oh where is the heather
The purple heather
Where is the heather
I loved so well?

GROUSE: Oh where is the heather
        The purple heather
BOTH: Who can tell?

GROUSE: To be ever so clever
        'Twas my firm endeavour
        To find you some heather
        Of purple hue
        I strained every feather
        I flew hell for leather
        But find you some heather
        Of purple hue
        I was unable to do.
        Now whether the weather's
        Affected the heather
        Whether the weather's
        Too cold or too hot
        Whether the weather's
        Affected the heather
        I know not.

GROUSE:

To be ever so clever
'Twas my firm endeavour
To find you some heather
Of purple hue
I strained every feather
I flew hell for leather
But find you some heather
Of purple hue
I was unable to do.
Now whether the weather's
Affected the heather
Whether the weather's
Too cold or too hot
Whether the weather's
Affected the heather
I know not.

OLD MAN:

Oh where is the heather

The purple heather

Where is the heather

I loved so well?

Oh where is the heather

The purple heather

Who can tell?

GROUSE:
Oh where is the heather

The purple heather

Where is the heather

I loved so well?

Oh where is the heather

The purple heather

Who can tell?

OLD MAN:
To be ever so clever
'Twas your firm endeavour
To find me some heather
Of purple hue
You strained every feather
You flew hell for leather
But find me some heather
Of purple hue
You were unable to do.
Now whether the weather's
Affected the heather
Whether the weather's
Too cold or too hot
Whether the weather's
Affected the heather
You know not.

BOTH: Oh where is the heather
The purple heather
Who can tell?

[*As the song ends, the kettle boils, whistling in sympathy.*]

[THE OLD MAN *sits in stunned silence as* GROUSE *takes the kettle off the stove.*]

OLD MAN: I cannae believe it. You're sure?

GROUSE: As sure as this kettle is boiled. Now, I'll make your porridge.

OLD MAN: No, no. I've no appetite now, Grousy. I feel in my bones, something terrible, something ghastly going on, something unnatural, something horrible on our very doorstep...

[*A sudden knock. Both jump. From outside echoes a voice.*]

GIANT GORMLESS: [*off*] Fee, fi, fo ... fiddle! No, no. Fee, fo, fi ... no. Fi, fee, fo ... no ...

[THE OLD MAN *draws back the deerskin curtain.*

Outside stands GIANT GORMLESS. *He is not especially tall.*]

OLD MAN: Yes?

[GIANT GORMLESS *jumps.*]

GIANT GORMLESS: Oh! Sorry, you made me jump.

OLD MAN: Who are you?

GIANT GORMLESS: I'm a giant.

[*He comes in the cave.*]

OLD MAN: Really?

GIANT GORMLESS: Yes. Listen. [*tries again*] Fee, fi, fo … er …

OLD MAN: Fum?

GIANT GORMLESS: Eh?

OLD MAN: Fum?

GIANT GORMLESS: Ah! Yes! Thanks! Fee, fi, fo … tum! … no, no, not tum. Fee, fi, fo … bum! … no, botty! … potty! … oh, bother! … sorry.

OLD MAN: Something tells me you're not a real giant.

GIANT GORMLESS: I *am*. I'm very real.

[GROUSE *has been eyeing* GIANT GORMLESS *suspiciously from the stove.*]

GROUSE: He looks a wee bit wee to me.

GIANT GORMLESS: There's no need to be personal. Giants have feelings.

OLD MAN: No, no. She means, well … giants are traditionally somewhat taller than you, Mr …

GIANT GORMLESS: [*offended*] Mr? I'm *Giant* Gormless.

OLD MAN: Gormless?

GIANT GORMLESS: Gormless, yes. I am a skilled and celebrated Gorm-catcher.

[*He presents his card to* THE OLD MAN.]

OLD MAN: Gorm-catcher?

GIANT GORMLESS: Catcher of Gorms, yes.

OLD MAN: Then why are you called 'Gorm*less*'?

GIANT GORMLESS: I haven't caught one yet.

OLD MAN: Thank goodness.

GIANT GORMLESS: It's not fair!

OLD MAN: It most certainly isn't. It's disgraceful.

GIANT GORMLESS: It is. I've been searching for days and I haven't even *seen* a Gorm yet.

OLD MAN: I hope you never shall. How dare you! Gorm-catcher, indeed. What have those innocent creatures ever done to you?

GIANT GORMLESS: Nothing.

OLD MAN: Exactly.

GIANT GORMLESS: It's not what they've done *to* me, it's what they're going to do *for* me.

OLD MAN: For you?

Song Three: **Gathering Gorms**

GIANT GORMLESS: You've heard of gathering mushrooms
You've heard of gathering storms
You've heard of gathering nuts in May
Well, I go gathering Gorms!

Ha Ha! Hee Hee! Ho Ho Ho!

Gorms, Gorms
I'm coming to find you
Gorms, Gorms
I've made up my mind to
Trap you and snatch you
And grab you and catch you
Then I won't be gormless no more!

Ha! Hee Hee! Ho Ho Ho!

Gorms, Gorms
I may not have met you
Yet, but
I'm coming to get you
Bet you I'll net you
Upset you — then pet you!
And I won't be gormless no more.

OLD MAN: [*spoken*] But why Gorms? What on earth do you want them for?

GIANT GORMLESS: Aha!

[*sings*]
I've heard they're great physical jerkers
I'll train them to be little workers
They're bigger than fleas
You can see them with ease
I'll make them perform in my circus!

OLD MAN: [*spoken*] Circus? Performing Gorms? Disgraceful!
[*He strides angrily to* GIANT GORMLESS *and attempts to evict him.* GIANT GORMLESS *trips* THE OLD MAN *or pushes him to the floor.*]

GIANT GORMLESS: [*sings*] Ha Ha! Hee Hee! Ho Ho Ho!

I'll prove
I'm no ignoramus
Gorms will
Make me rich and famous
Honoured, respected,
No longer neglected,
I'll never be gormless again!

Ha! Hee Hee! Ho Ho Ho!

OLD MAN: I've heard enough. Gorm-napper! Out! Out of my cave!
[*He bundles* GIANT GORMLESS *to the doorway.*]
GIANT GORMLESS: But I need your assistance.
OLD MAN: You need a knock on the nose! Out! Gormless you are, and Gormless may you stay. Good riddance!
[GIANT GORMLESS *goes.* THE OLD MAN *returns, enervated.*]
You know what this means, Grousy?
GROUSE: Aye. It means your breakfast's gone cold.
OLD MAN: Breakfast? How can I stuff my stomach while the Gorms are in danger?
GROUSE: Oh, come on! You don't believe in Gorms?
OLD MAN: I most certainly do.
GROUSE: Then you're as gormless as that wee Giant! It's all a load of Highland twaddle.
OLD MAN: But Grousy, don't you see? The purple heather!
GROUSE: I only see the white heather.
OLD MAN: Exactly! There's no purple heather, because the Gorms don't dare venture forth to spray it from their heathercraft. They sense danger. Giant Gormless.
GROUSE: Last call for breakfast.
OLD MAN: I must help them.
GROUSE: Right, I'll have it.

> [*She sits down and eats.* THE OLD MAN *puts on his scarf and his tam-o'-shanter.*]

OLD MAN: I'll go away. Like you suggested. On an expedition to rescue the Gorms.

> [*He goes to the doorway.*]

GROUSE: How? You don't know where they live any more than Giant Gormless.

OLD MAN: [*stopping*] True.

> [*He returns, thinking.*]

GROUSE: You're right.

OLD MAN: Eh?

GROUSE: My cousin lays a very good egg.

> [*She continues to tuck in.*]

OLD MAN: [*having an idea*] Lagopus Scoticus!

GROUSE: Don't you call me rude names!

OLD MAN: I'm not, you stupid bird. Lagopus Scoticus. The King of the Loch. He knows everything about everything. He'll lead me to the Gorms.

> [*He starts to go.*]

GROUSE: You'd better take your overnight bag.

> [*She finds it and gives it to* THE OLD MAN — *a commodious leather hold-all 'grip'.*]

It's all packed.

OLD MAN: Thank you, Grousy.

> [*He starts to go.*]

GROUSE: And take your heather porridge. Swimming makes you hungry.

> [*She puts a lid on the porridge bowl and puts it in the overnight bag.*]

OLD MAN: Thank you, Grousy.

> [*He starts to go.*]

GROUSE: [*pouring water from the kettle into a rubber hot-water bottle*] And the water'll be freezing. Take this.

OLD MAN: What?

GROUSE: Your water hot-bot.

OLD MAN: Thank you, Grousy.

> [*He tucks it in his jacket, starts to go, then turns.*]

Would you like to come too?

GROUSE: Certainly not. I've got far too much grousework to do!

OLD MAN: Then, farewell!

GROUSE: [*softer*] Good luck, Old Man! May *you* fare well!

> [THE OLD MAN *exits through the doorway.* GROUSE *holds open the deerskin door.* THE OLD MAN *dives into the loch.*]
>
> [*Loud splash.*]
>
> [*Blackout.*]

SCENE TWO — Under the Loch

During the scene change THE OLD MAN's *splash leads into the bubbly music of underwater bagpipes.*

Lights up on the loch bottom. A gauze and rippling lighting effects. Tall, thin loch plants dancing in the water.

The bagpipe music continues as THE OLD MAN *enters, searching for* LAGOPUS SCOTICUS. *He is met by* TWO NAGAR MAIDS — *freshwater mermaids. They beckon him. He follows.*

Enter LAGOPUS SCOTICUS, *a freshwater variant of Neptune. He sits on a throne on a raised dais. A musical fanfare greets him. Meanwhile he continues to drone on, playing his bagpipes.*

THE NAGAR MAIDS *and* THE OLD MAN *bow politely. The bagpipes stop and* THE OLD MAN *steps forward. He speaks (if the sound department can so engineer it) in a bubbly voice.*

OLD MAN: Your Royal Freshwater Highness, I ...

> [*The bagpipes start again — it was a false ending. After a few bars they stop.*]

I have come, your Royal Fresh ...

> [*The bagpipes start again. After a few bars they*

stop. THE OLD MAN *dares not speak in case of interruption again.*]

[*Pause.*]

LAGOPUS SCOTICUS: Well, Old Man? Why have you come to see us? Can't wait all morning.

OLD MAN: Ah, yes, of course, your Royal Highwater Freshness ...

LAGOPUS SCOTICUS: Spit it out!

OLD MAN: I request your Freshness's royal aid.

LAGOPUS SCOTICUS: Ade? What sort of ade? Lemonade? Cherryade?

OLD MAN: No, sir, *your* aid.

LAGOPUS SCOTICUS: Our ade? You greedy Old Man, drink your own!

OLD MAN: No, sir, your aid, your help.

LAGOPUS SCOTICUS: Ah. Sorry, Old Man. We never give help on an empty stomach. The royal motto.

OLD MAN: [*having an idea and taking out his breakfast*] Please, sir, I would be honoured if you would share my breakfast. Heather porridge.

LAGOPUS SCOTICUS: [*unsure*] Well ...

OLD MAN: With clover juice.

LAGOPUS SCOTICUS: [*convinced*] Mmm. Thank you.

[*He takes one of his bagpipes and uses it as a straw. A loud sucking noise.*]

Delicious.

[*Another slurping suck. He is interrupted by a bubbly hunting horn blast.* THE OLD MAN *jumps.*]

OLD MAN: What's that?

LAGOPUS SCOTICUS: Tally-hoo! Time for our morning hunt.

OLD MAN: Hunt?

LAGOPUS SCOTICUS: Come and join us. Hunt the Loch-haggis!

OLD MAN: But I ... oh dear!

[*Music.*]

LAGOPUS SCOTICUS: Weapons!

[THE NAGAR MAIDS *bring large nets and hand* LAGOPUS SCOTICUS *his trident, which has been leaning against his throne.*]

Pipe in the haggis!

[LAGOPUS SCOTICUS *plays on his bagpipes.*

Enter THREE LOCH-HAGGIS, *small, round, giggly creatures who move in a circular fashion because one leg is longer than the other. They cock cheery snooks at* LAGOPUS SCOTICUS *and* THE OLD MAN *and make rude noises at them.*]

Song Four: **Hunt the Haggis**

[*A choreographed haggis-hunt, during which* LAGOPUS SCOTICUS *and* THE OLD MAN *chase* THE LOCH-HAGGIS. *At first they are unsuccessful.* THE OLD MAN *trips over his net.* THE LOCH-HAGGIS *giggle at him and tickle him.* LAGOPUS SCOTICUS *chases them off. They hide behind the throne.*]

ALL: Hunt the haggis
Hunt the haggis
Yoiks and tally-hoo!
Hunt the haggis
Hunt the haggis
LOCH-HAGGIS: Yah boo sucks to you!

ALL: Hunt the haggis
Hunt the haggis
Juicy, ripe and plump
Hunt the haggis
Hunt the haggis
Boo!
LOCH-HAGGIS: You made us jump!

ALL: See them hop and see them run
The hunting season has begun
Race 'em, chase 'em 'til they're caught
Join the wonder of our underwater sport.

Hunt the haggis
Hunt the haggis
Take 'em by surprise
Hunt the haggis
Hunt the haggis
Win yourself a prize!

Hunt the haggis
Hunt the haggis
Leading us a dance
Hunt the haggis
Hunt the haggis
LOCH-HAGGIS: You don't stand a chance!

ALL: Hear them giggle, hear them squeal
See them dance a haggis reel
They enjoy it, so do we
Fun for ev'ryone, the haggis hunting spree.

Hunt the haggis
Hunt the haggis
LOCH-HAGGIS: Catch us if you can!
ALL: Hunt the haggis
Hunt the haggis
OLD MAN: I've a canny plan...

[THE OLD MAN *mimes that he has an idea. He takes the remains of his heather porridge and lays it as bait. A trail. Then he hides with his net.* LAGOPUS SCOTICUS *watches as* THE LOCH-HAGGIS *greedily eat the heather porridge, ending up in a munching cluster.* THE OLD MAN *emerges and nets them triumphantly.*]

ALL: Hunt the haggis
Hunt the haggis
Beaten fair and square!
Hunt the haggis
Hunt the haggis
LOCH-HAGGIS: Boo! It wasn't fair!
[*Fanfare.*]
LAGOPUS SCOTICUS: Brilliant! Masterly! We congratulate you, Old Man. You deserve a prize!
OLD MAN: A prize?
LAGOPUS SCOTICUS: You win — a thrace of Loch-haggis!
[THE NAGAR MAIDS *applaud.*]
OLD MAN: What?
LAGOPUS SCOTICUS: [*lifting the net*] There! They are all yours to take home.

OLD MAN: Oh, but I don't ...
> [THE LOCH-HAGGIS *squeal with delight and nuzzle affectionately against* THE OLD MAN.]

... yes, well ... thank you ...
> [*He is tickled.*]

Ooh! Stop it! Behave!
> [THE LOCH-HAGGIS *giggle.*]

LOCH-HAGGIS: [*echoing* THE OLD MAN] Stop it! Behave!
> [*They giggle.*]

LAGOPUS SCOTICUS: [*returning to his throne*] Now, Old Man. What can we do to help you? Speak.

OLD MAN: Thank you, sir.
> [*He stands formally.*]

Your Royal Freshwater Highness. The Gorms are in danger. Please tell me how to find the wee creatures and offer them my assistance.

LAGOPUS SCOTICUS: Mm. Gorms.
> [*He thinks, then looks in an ancient tome under his throne.*]

Gimbles, Gollops, Gumbies ... no, too far, ... aha! Gorms. [*reads, muttering*] Mm. [*calls*] Map!
> [A NAGAR MAID *produces a map, which she gives to* THE OLD MAN.]

Use this to find your way. [*calls*] Potion!
> [A NAGAR MAID *produces a small bottle and gives it to* THE OLD MAN.]

Drink this.
> [THE OLD MAN *goes to drink.*]

Not now, you silly old man. Remember ...

Song Five: **The Potion**

When you reach the Gorms' front door
Drink the potion and not before.

OLD MAN: [*committing the rhyme to memory*]
'When you reach the Gorms' front door
Drink the potion and not before.'
Thank you, sir, most kind.
> [*He puts the potion in his overnight bag.*]

LOCH-HAGGIS: [*echoing* THE OLD MAN] Most kind! Most kind!
[*They giggle.*]
LAGOPUS SCOTICUS: Fortune go with you! Farewell!
OLD MAN: Farewell!
LOCH-HAGGIS: Farewell! Farewell!
[*They giggle.*]

[*Music as* LAGOPUS SCOTICUS *and* THE NAGAR MAIDS *exit.*]

[*The gauze descends and* THE OLD MAN *and* THE LOCH-HAGGIS *appear to rise to the surface. They step downstage as though climbing on to the bank of the loch.* THE OLD MAN *consults the map, 'assisted' by the* LOCH-HAGGIS, *who all point different suggestions as to which direction to take.* THE OLD MAN *decides and they set off on a stylised walk.*]

[*Meanwhile the scene changes to...*]

SCENE THREE — A Rock

A largish (say four feet high), flattish rock, surrounded by white heather.

THE OLD MAN *and* THE LOCH-HAGGIS *approach the rock as the lights come up.*

OLD MAN: Haggis, halt!
[THE LOCH-HAGGIS *bump into each other and fall over, giggling.*]
Now. [*looking at the map*] Let me see, where are we?
[THE LOCH-HAGGIS *search everywhere, independently, looking on the ground, behind the rock.*]
LOCH-HAGGIS: Let me see, where are we? Let me see, where are we? Let me see, where are we? [*etc.*]
[*They all meet each other in a clump.*]
Here we are! Here we are!
[*They giggle.*]
OLD MAN: Quiet! You hopeless Haggis.

[THE LOCH-HAGGIS *stop, offended.*]

You've less brain than a half-baked haddock.

[THE LOCH-HAGGIS *giggle.*]

LOCH-HAGGIS 1: Less brain ...

LOCH-HAGGIS 2: ... than a half-baked

LOCH-HAGGIS 3: ... haddock!

LOCH-HAGGIS 2: Haddock!

LOCH-HAGGIS 1: Haddock!

ALL THREE: Mm, mmm, yummy hummy haddock, mmm... [*etc.*]

[*They pat their stomachs.*]

OLD MAN: You're hungry?

LOCH-HAGGIS: Mmm. Hungry. Mmm.

OLD MAN: This is not a time to think of food. We have to follow the map.

LOCH-HAGGIS: Map, map! Yummy, yummy! Map, map! Tasty, tasty!

[*They grab the map from* THE OLD MAN *and try to eat it.*]

OLD MAN: No, no! Not swallow it! Follow it!

LOCH-HAGGIS: Ohhh! Follow, not swallow! Not swallow, follow!

OLD MAN: Give it to me!

[*He takes the map and studies it.*]

See? Follow the map!

LOCH-HAGGIS: Follow, follow! Follow, follow!

OLD MAN: Yes. Now, let's see.

[*He wanders off, looking at the map.* THE LOCH-HAGGIS *follow.* THE OLD MAN *stops.* THE LOCH-HAGGIS *bump into him.*]

Ahhh! What are you doing now?

LOCH-HAGGIS: Following the map! Following the map!

[*They giggle.*]

OLD MAN: What you need is a bit of discipline.

[THE LOCH-HAGGIS *search each other for a bit of discipline.*]

LOCH-HAGGIS: Bit of discipline? Bit of discipline?

[*Eventually they face* THE OLD MAN.]

LOCH-HAGGIS 1: No!

LOCH-HAGGIS 2: No discipline!

LOCH-HAGGIS 3: Not even a bit!

[*They giggle.*]

OLD MAN: Mm. So I see. Now, stand straight and listen for your names. [*realising he doesn't know them*] What are your names? Do Haggis have names?

LOCH-HAGGIS: [*consulting with each other*] Names? Haggis have names?

[*Eventually they face* THE OLD MAN.]

Yes!

LOCH-HAGGIS 1: Me Aggie.

OLD MAN: Ah. Aggie. Hallo.

LOCH-HAGGIS 2: Me Maggie.

OLD MAN: Hallo, Maggie.

LOCH-HAGGIS 3: Me...

OLD MAN: Let me guess. You must be ... Baggie?

[THE LOCH-HAGGIS *shake their heads vigorously.*]

Saggie?

[*Another shake.*]

Er ... Craggie?

[*Another shake.*]

I give up.

LOCH-HAGGIS 3: Hamish.

[THE LOCH-HAGGIS *collapse into giggles.*]

OLD MAN: Hamish.

[*More giggles.*]

I see. Aggie, Maggie and Hamish. Right. Now then, Aggie, Maggie and Hamish. What do you know about Gorms?

LOCH-HAGGIS: [*chanting*]

We love Gorms, boiled or roast,
Fried in batter or Gorms on toast
Barbecued for Sunday tea
Gorms are good for you and me!

[*They giggle.*]

OLD MAN: No, no, no! Gorms are friendly creatures. You can't eat them.

LOCH-HAGGIS: [*disappointed*] Oh.

OLD MAN: They're in danger. We have to rescue them. From...

[*He is interrupted by the sound of singing from offstage.*]

Song Six: **Gorm Call (Fee, Fi)**

GIANT GORMLESS: Fee, Fi, Fo, Fum
Gorms get ready, here I come!

OLD MAN: It's Gormless! Quick! Hide, Haggis!
[THE OLD MAN *and* THE LOCH-HAGGIS *scramble behind the rock after a certain amount of confusion and bumping into each other.*]

[*Enter* GIANT GORMLESS.]

Song Six (continued)

GIANT GORMLESS: Fee, Fi, Fo ... Ohhh!

[*spoken*] Where are they? Where are they? For days I've trudged the Lowlands and Highlands, no Trossach untrod, no cliff unclimbed, no loch unlooked in, but not a single sniff, not a single glimpse of a Gorm ...
[*He sees the rock.*]
Aha! An unexplored rock!
[*Tension music as he creeps round the rock.* THE OLD MAN *and* THE LOCH-HAGGIS *emerge at the other end and, crouching, go round the front as* GIANT GORMLESS *goes round the back. They put their fingers to their lips as if to tell* THE AUDIENCE *not to give them away. They return behind the rock as* GIANT GORMLESS *emerges round the front.*]
Nothing! Nothing!
[*A sudden giggle from* A LOCH-HAGGIS *is heard, followed by a 'Shhh!'*]
What was that? [*seeing* THE AUDIENCE] Aha! Tourists! Excuse me, dear friends, but did you just hear something?
[*Heads over the rock shake, asking* THE AUDIENCE *to say 'No'.*]

AUDIENCE: No.
GIANT GORMLESS: I think you did. Didn't you?
AUDIENCE: No.

GIANT GORMLESS: It was a Gorm, wasn't it?

AUDIENCE: No.

GIANT GORMLESS: It was!

AUDIENCE: It wasn't!

GIANT GORMLESS: Was.

AUDIENCE: Wasn't!

GIANT GORMLESS: Mm. I see. But if you *do* hear — or see — a Gorm, you will tell me, won't you?

[*Either:*]   [*Or:*]

AUDIENCE: Yes.   AUDIENCE: No.

GIANT GORMLESS: Thank you!   GIANT GORMLESS: You rotten lot! I'll catch *you* and turn you all into performing tourists if you don't look out.

[GIANT GORMLESS *exits.*]

[*calling*] Gorms! Where are you? Gorms!

[*He has gone.* THE OLD MAN *and* THE LOCH-HAGGIS *emerge.*]

OLD MAN: [*to* THE AUDIENCE] Thank you. Most kind.

LOCH-HAGGIS: [*echoing*] Thank you. Most kind.

OLD MAN: Shhh! We must be off and away. [*noticing*] Ah! Where's my overnight bag? [*remembering*] Behind the rock. Fetch it oot while I check the route.

LOCH-HAGGIS: Oot, route, oot, route! [*going behind the rock*] Bag. Bag. Bag.

[THE OLD MAN *spreads out the map and kneels down to peruse it.*]

OLD MAN: Now then …

[THE LOCH-HAGGIS *return with the overnight bag. Seeing* THE OLD MAN *is not looking, they open it, giggling. One takes out a nightgown and holds it up. The second finds a nightcap and puts it on. The third finds a teddy bear, complete with kilt, and holds it, sucking his thumb. More giggles.* THE OLD MAN *turns.*]

What are you doing? That's my nightie! And my nightcap! And my best teddy! Put them back, you horrible Haggis.

[*Giggling,* THE LOCH-HAGGIS *put the things back.* THE OLD MAN *is back with his map.*]

[THE LOCH-HAGGIS *bring out the potion and look at it. They fancy a drink. One beckons and they all go behind the rock. We see them each drink. The last puts the potion bottle on the rock.*]

[*A sudden loud deflating noise.* THE LOCH-HAGGIS *appear to shrink until they disappear behind the rock.*]

[*folding the map and getting up*] Right. We go in *that* direction ... [*looking round*] Haggis, where are you? Stop playing. [*to* THE AUDIENCE] Where are they?

AUDIENCE: Behind the rock!

OLD MAN: Where?

AUDIENCE: Behind the rock!

               [THE OLD MAN *goes to the rock and sees the potion bottle.*]

OLD MAN: [*with a gasp*] They didn't drink this, did they?

AUDIENCE: Yes!

OLD MAN: But that was only to be drunk when ...

[*He remembers what* LAGOPUS SCOTICUS *had said.*]

'When you reach the Gorms' front door
Drink the potion and not before.'

[*He rushes round behind the rock. Suddenly three miniature versions of* THE LOCH-HAGGIS *appear on the rock. (It is suggested that these are glove-puppets, say eighteen inches high, operated from inside the rock by the actors playing* THE LOCH HAGGIS.*)*]

[THE AUDIENCE *notices them before* THE OLD MAN *and probably tells him.*]

[THE PUPPET-LOCH-HAGGIS *giggle and jiggle about.*]

[THE OLD MAN *stands behind the rock and sees them.*]

What? I don't believe ... They've shrunk! Did you drink the potion, you naughty wee Haggis?

[THE PUPPET-LOCH-HAGGIS *nod and giggle.*]
All of it?

[*They shake their heads as* THE OLD MAN *looks at the potion bottle.*]

No, there's a little left. I hope it'll be enough for me.
Well, I cannae leave you here. There's nothing for it.
My overnight bag.

[*Squeals of protest as* THE OLD MAN *removes* THE PUPPET-LOCH-HAGGIS *from the rock and puts them inside his bag. The squeals become muffled.*]

And don't squash my teddy!

[*Music as* THE OLD MAN *snaps shut the overnight bag and starts walking — a stylised walk as the scene changes to...*]

SCENE FOUR — A High Crag

As the scene changes, the lighting changes to suggest night-time. THE OLD MAN *becomes more and more tired.*

Music continues as he climbs up the crag, sinks to the ground, still clutching the map and the overnight bag, and falls asleep, snoring and whistling loudly.

After a pause, the music becomes more sinister as GIANT GORMLESS *enters through the shadows. He shines a torch and sees* THE OLD MAN *asleep.* THE AUDIENCE *may well try to wake* THE OLD MAN *but with no success.* GIANT GORMLESS *climbs up the crag and comes to* THE OLD MAN. *He sees the map. He takes it, studies it with his torch, and sees what he hopes to see.*

GIANT GORMLESS: Gorm Grotto!

[*He hurries down the crag and exits, taking the map with him.*]

[*After a pause,* THE OLD MAN *wakes and starts to get up, though he is still exhausted.*]

OLD MAN: Must travel onward! Must travel onward!

[*He suddenly notices his map has disappeared.*]

My map!

[THE AUDIENCE *shouts out the information.*]

What? Stolen? By whom?

AUDIENCE: Giant Gormless!

OLD MAN: Giant Gormless?

AUDIENCE: Yes.

OLD MAN: Which way did he go? This way?

AUDIENCE: No.

OLD MAN: That way?

AUDIENCE: Yes.

OLD MAN: Thank you!

[*As he starts to go, he is interrupted by a sudden noise: the very loud beating of wings, from up above. He looks up and gasps.*]

Aaah! 'Tis the Pig-eagle!

[*Grunting noises are heard along with the beating of wings. The noises grow louder.* THE OLD MAN *cowers.*]

[*Suddenly, from above,* THE PIG-EAGLE *flies into view through the darkness — a very large bird with outstretched wings, and a pig's head with eyes lit up and flashing. The terrifying shape of* THE PIG-EAGLE *descends towards* THE OLD MAN, *the noises growing louder.*]

No! No! Put me down! He...lp!

[*Blackout, as the noises grow even louder and change to 'Whooshing-through-the-air' noises.*]

END OF ACT ONE

ACT TWO

SCENE ONE — The Sky

A shadow-puppet sequence against a screen or a U.V. sequence using puppets with the real OLD MAN *against a black background.*

Music, as THE PIG-EAGLE *carries* THE OLD MAN (*still clutching his overnight bag*) *up above the jutting crags and peaks of the mountain.*

OLD MAN: [*voice-over*] Help! Pig-eagle, put me down!

Song Seven: **The Pig-eagle**

> [*During the song, other birds fly past and look at* THE PIG-EAGLE *and* THE OLD MAN *in surprise.*]

> [*In blue evening light they pass over the mountain of Lochnagar and the turrets of Balmoral.*]

VOICES-OVER: On the mountain top lives a creature who's
Not entered in ref'rence books or found in zoos
You will seldom ever see him, if you do go hide
Or he'll pounce and you'll be taken for a ride

By the Pig-eagle
(Pig-eagle)
Sweeping the skies
With his mighty wings
And his piggy eagle eyes
Yes the Pig-eagle
(Pig-eagle)
Out on the hunt
Hear his fearful snuffle
And his blood-curdling grunt.

A snout sticks out, not a beak or bill
His trotters have talons and he dines on swill
On a high rocky ledge he nests in a sty
Living proof of the legend that pigs can fly.

See the Pig-eagle
(Pig-eagle)
Sweeping the skies
With his mighty wings
And his piggy eagle eyes
See the Pig-eagle
(Pig-eagle)
Out on the hunt
Hear his fearful snuffle
And his blood-curdling grunt.

Was his father a bird?
Was his mother a sow?
His hist'ry is a myst'ry
He was born, but how? (But how?)

He squeals like a pig yet he swoops like a hawk
Not a bird of prey, more a bird of pork
When the sun goes down in the highland sky
If they hear a distant snort the crofters cry —

'Tis the Pig-eagle
(Pig-eagle)
Sweeping the skies
With his mighty wings
And his piggy eagle eyes
'Tis the Pig-eagle
(Pig-eagle)
Out on the hunt
Hear his fearful snuffle
And his blood-curdling grunt.

'Tis the Pig-eagle
The Pig-eagle
The Pig-eagle ...

> [*As the song ends,* THE PIG-EAGLE *grunts and lets go of* THE OLD MAN, *who, tossing and turning, hurtles down towards earth* ...]
>
> [*A whistling noise suggests his fall, then cuts out suddenly.*]
>
> [*Blackout.*]
>
> [*A loud crashing noise.*]

SCENE TWO — The Entrance to Gorm Grotto

THE OLD MAN is sprawled on a clump of heather, his overnight bag lying nearby. It is morning.

On one side of the stage is a rock about three feet high. Half of it is offstage.

The main feature is a mountain face (possibly a cloth), in which is a small aperture, say eighteen inches high, with a sign above — just large enough for THE AUDIENCE *to read: 'Gorm Grotto'.*

THE OLD MAN sits up and dusts himself off.

OLD MAN: [*shaking his fist at the sky*] Perishing Pig-eagle! Most untrustworthy creature. Dropping me in the midst of nowhere. [*getting up*] Where on earth am I?
> [*Hopefully* THE AUDIENCE *will shout out 'Gorm Grotto'. If not,* THE OLD MAN *finds the sign and asks* THE AUDIENCE *to read it.*]

AUDIENCE: Gorm Grotto.

OLD MAN: Where?

AUDIENCE: Gorm Grotto.

OLD MAN: Suffering sporrans, you're right! [*looking up at the sky*] Thank you for the lift, Pig-eagle. Apologies, I misjudged you. [*to* THE AUDIENCE] Most trustworthy creature.
> [*A muffled giggling is heard.*]

What's that noise? Of course, the wee Loch-haggis! Where's my overnight bag?
> [*Perhaps* THE AUDIENCE *will lead him to it.*]

Thank you.
> [*He opens the bag. The giggles grow louder.*]

Hallo, Haggis! Are you all right? Out you come.
> [*He takes them out and puts them on the rock at the side. The hands of the actors playing* THE LOCH-HAGGIS *meet* THE PUPPETS *and operate.*]

Hallo, Aggie! There. Out you come, Maggie! That's the way. Now you, Hamish.
> [*He brings out his teddy by mistake.*]

No, no! Not you, Teddy. Where's Hamish? There

you are. Now, you'd better all have a wee stretch after your flight.

> [*Giggles and physical jerks from* THE PUPPET-LOCH-HAGGIS.]

> [THE OLD MAN *takes his overnight bag over to the entrance to the grotto. He bends down to look inside.*]

How in the name of Lochnagar do I get in there?

AUDIENCE: Drink the potion!
OLD MAN: I beg your pardon?
AUDIENCE: Drink the potion!
OLD MAN: Of course! You're right! Just as Lagopus Scoticus said.

Song Seven 'a': **The Potion** (*reprise*)

When you reach the Gorms' front door
Drink the potion and not before.

Right.

> [*Music continues as he finds the potion in the overnight bag.*]

Ready, steady, drink!

> [*He drinks.*]

Ugh!

> [*Exciting sound effects as a magical transformation takes place. It is as though* THE OLD MAN *is shrinking. Flashing lights may help the illusion.*]

> [THE PUPPET-LOCH-HAGGIS *disappear as the rock on which they perch appears to grow. (This could be achieved by sliding the rock further on stage; the further it appears the wider and higher it should be.)*]

> [*Meanwhile the clump of heather grows into a jungle about three feet high, and the aperture in the mountain face appears to grow (and the sign) four- or five-fold. (The cloth could possibly be a gauze, through which the enlarged version becomes visible.)*]

[*As the transformation takes place,* THE OLD MAN *cries out.*]

I'm shrinking, I'm shrinking!

[*He reacts as though buffeted by the power of the potion. He falls over.*]

[*When the transformation is complete, he looks up and sees the entrance to Gorm Grotto, now accessible.*]

Extraordinary! Amazing!

[*Loud giggles herald the appearance, from behind the rock, of* THE LOCH-HAGGIS (*original size*).]

Hallo, Haggis!

[*They cluster round him.*]

Och, it's good to see you up to size again.

[THE LOCH-HAGGIS *noisily voice the fact that he is wrong. They mime the fact that they have not grown; he has shrunk!*]

What? Oh, I see! You've not grown. *I've* shrunk! Yes, of course. Come on, then. Time to warn the Gorms.

LOCH-HAGGIS: [*excited*] Gorm the warns, warm the Gorms, gorn the warms ... [*etc.*]

OLD MAN: Shh! Behave! Follow me!

LOCH-HAGGIS 1: [*to* LOCH-HAGGIS 2] Follow me!

LOCH-HAGGIS 2: [*to* LOCH-HAGGIS 3] Follow me!

LOCH-HAGGIS 3: [*to* NOBODY] Follow me!

[*Giggles. All approach the grotto entrance.*]

[*Suddenly the lighting dims. Ominous music and sound effects as* A HUGE SPIDER (*an actor in costume*) *enters from above or from offstage.* THE AUDIENCE *should shout a warning.* THE OLD MAN *and* THE LOCH-HAGGIS *see* THE SPIDER.]

[*Pandemonium as* THE SPIDER *tries to catch them.* THE LOCH-HAGGIS *try to flee, but* THE SPIDER *catches them and clings on to them with its furry legs.* THE OLD MAN *manages to prise the legs away and release* THE LOCH-HAGGIS, *but nearly gets caught himself.*]

[*Finally they manage to chase* THE SPIDER *away, or he retreats upwards. Hastily* THE OLD MAN *and* THE LOCH-HAGGIS *start to enter Gorm Grotto.*]

[*Blackout.*]

SCENE THREE — Inside Gorm Grotto

A spacious cave. The entrance, a tunnel in the rock, leads offstage. Tall thistle plants grow as decoration. Posters advertising the 'Gorm Games' have 'Cancelled' signs pasted over them. A throne carved from rock is upstage, facing downstage. The cave has been fitted out as a Gorm gymnasium, with various keep-fit devices — wallbars, weights, a trapeze perhaps. Purple mats. Large hoops. Perhaps a trampoline. The predominant colour is purple.

As the lights come up the grotto is a hive of activity. The Gorms — dressed in purple — are performing acrobatic feats. Music accompanies their somersaults, dives through hoops, trampolining, trapeze-work, etc. Rather like a circus act they perform tricks, applaud each other and generally display their considerable skills.

Song Eight: **Get up and go go**

GORMS Get up get a move on
+ VOICES-OVER: Get up out of bed
Get up and get at it
Get ready get set
Arms stretch, breathe in, through your nose
Breathe out, knees bend, touch your toes
Yes, get it together, do your bit!
Get up and go go
Get fit!

Go go
Get up and go go go go
No no
Don't be a no no no no

Go go
Get up and go go go go
Up down up down
Like a yo yo
Get up and go go go go go.

Get leaping and bouncing
Go run on the spot
Elastic, gymnastic
Give it all you got
Hop skip, back flip, forward roll
Cartwheel, spring heel, go for goal!
Yes, get it together, go for it!
Get up and go go
Get fit!

Go go
Get up and go go go go
No no
Don't be a no no no no
Go go
Get up and go go go go
Up down up down
Like a yo yo
Get up and go go go go go.

Get into the action
Get out of your chair
Get happy get healthy
Jump up in the air
Over, under, loop the loop
Flying, diving through a hoop
Yes get it together, don't just sit!
Get up and go go
Get fit!

Go go
Get up and go go go go
No no
Don't be a no no no no
Go go
Get up and go go go go

Up down up down
Like a yo yo
Go go
Get up and go go go go
No no
Don't be a no no no no
Go go
Get up and go go go go
Up down up down
Like a yo-yo
Get up and go go go go go go go.

[*After a two- or three-minute routine, enter, furtively,* THE OLD MAN *and* THE LOCH-HAGGIS. *Intrigued, they watch the display, which perhaps ends up with a* GORM *pyramid: three on the floor, two on their shoulders, one on top.*]

[THE OLD MAN, *impressed, applauds.*]

OLD MAN: Bravo! Bravo!

[THE GORMS *see him and the pyramid collapses.*]

GORM 1: Trespassers!

GORM 2: Intruders!

GORM 3: Strangers!

GORM 4: Gate-crashers!

GORM 5: Invaders!

OLD MAN: No, no, really. I assure you ...

GORM 6: Sound the alarm!

[A GORM *punches a set of bagpipes hanging like a punchball. This sets off a droning alarm call.*]

[THE LOCH-HAGGIS *scatter in alarm;* THE OLD MAN *protests. But the wiry* GORMS *catch all four in the hoops through which they were somersaulting seconds before. Holding on to the hoops,* THE GORMS *gormhandle their captives up towards the throne.*]

[*The alarm stops.*]

GORM 1: Summon the Queen!

GORM 2: Summon the Queen!

GORM 3: Summon the Queen!

GORM 4: Summon the Queen!

[*Leaving* GORMS 1, 2, 3 *and* 4 *with the prisoners,* GORMS 5 *and* 6 *go to fetch* THE QUEEN *from offstage — the side opposite the entrance to the cave.*]

OLD MAN: Please listen, we ...

GORMS 1, 2, 3 & 4: Silence!

GORMS 5 & 6: The Queen!

[*Fanfare. With pomp and ceremony, they lead in the* GORM QUEEN. *She is very fat, wearing a purple robe and crown.*]

Song Nine: **The Gorm Anthem**

[THE OLD MAN *and* THE LOCH-HAGGIS *can join in as appropriate.*]

GORMS: Small in size but
Big in heart
Gorms love games
And treacle tart
Always there
Though seldom seen
Long live Gorms
Long live our Queen.

Gorms are wee
(With a double 'e')
May our days
Be trouble-free
May we bravely
Face life's storms
Long live our Queen
Long live Gorms.

May we bravely
Face life's storms
Long live our Queen
Long live Gorms.

[THE GORMS *bow as a sign of respect and force their captives to do the same.*]

[THE QUEEN *stands in front of her throne and looks extremely serious and implacable.*]

QUEEN: What roguery is here?

GORM 1: Trespassers!

GORM 2: Intruders!

GORM 3: Strangers!

GORM 4: Gate-crashers!

GORM 5: Invaders!

OLD MAN: Please, your Gormness, we ...

GORM 6: Trespassers will be executed!

OLD MAN: Executed? But really, we ...

QUEEN: Silence! This is most serious.

OLD MAN: It is indeed, your Gormship, we came here to ...

QUEEN: Enough! I must deliberate. Throne!

[GORMS 5 *and* 6 *lift the overweight* QUEEN *onto the seat of the throne, which is slightly too high for easy self-reaching. It also slopes down somewhat.*]

Thank you.

[GORMS 5 *and* 6 *stand aside.*]

I ...

[*Suddenly* THE QUEEN *slides down the seat and lands with a bump on the floor.*]

Aaaaah! Ow!

[THE LOCH-HAGGIS *giggle.* THE GORMS *try to hush them.*]

Blasted throne! A plague on it! [*to* GORMS 5 *and* 6]
Well, don't just stand there. Get me up!

[GORMS 5 *and* 6 *lift* THE QUEEN *onto the throne, then stand aside.* THE QUEEN *composes herself.*]

Trespassers will ...

[*Suddenly she slides down the seat again and lands heavily on the floor.*]

Aaaaah! Ow!

[THE LOCH-HAGGIS *giggle. This time* THE GORMS *can't help joining in.*]

Go on, then. Have a good giggle.

[*General laughter — but* THE OLD MAN *is concerned. He releases himself from the hoop*

and his giggling guard, steps forward and helps
THE QUEEN *to her feet.*]

OLD MAN: Allow me, your Gormness ...

QUEEN: A right royal laughing-stock, that's all I am. Can't even sit on my own throne. No wonder nobody takes me seriously. Take last year's State Opening of the Gorm Parliament. Disaster. Arrive, sit down and plop, on the floor. Sniggers from the front benches. Hysterics from the back. So undignified.

OLD MAN: May I examine it, ma'am?

QUEEN: What's the point? The royal bottoms of my royal predecessors have by their royal presence polished it so perfectly for so many centuries that now 'tis more slippery than a ski-slope.

OLD MAN: I know what you need, ma'am.

QUEEN: A new throne is what I need, but, tradition, you know, tradition ...

OLD MAN: Indeed. Please, ma'am, your Gormship, accept ... this.

[*He produces his hot-water bottle.* THE GORM COURT *is stunned to silence.*]

QUEEN: And what, pray, is this?

OLD MAN: My water hot-bot.

QUEEN: Your water what-bot?

OLD MAN: My water hot-bot. 'Tis fashioned from rubber, ma'am. Guaranteed anti-slip. Slip-proof. Slip-free.

QUEEN: Really? May I try it?

OLD MAN: Be my guest.

[*He carefully places the hot-water bottle on the throne.*]

QUEEN: Throne!

[GORMS 5 *and* 6 *repeat their lifting routine.* THE QUEEN *sits. Tension music as all hold their breaths.* GORMS 5 *and* 6 *stand aside. Success!* THE QUEEN *doesn't slip.*]

[*Cheers and applause.*]
[*bouncing up and down with pleasure*] You've done it! You've done it! Thank you! [*suddenly*] Silence! Be it known that ... [*aside to* THE OLD MAN] Who are you?

OLD MAN: The Old Man of Lochnagar. And these are my Haggis.

LOCH-HAGGIS 1: Aggie.

LOCH-HAGGIS 2: Maggie.

OLD MAN: And...

LOCH-HAGGIS 3: Hamish.

QUEEN: Ah. Be it known that the Old Man of Lochnagar and his Haggis, in return for services rendered to the royal throne, I hereby, straightway, forthwith and for ever more grant a free pardon.

OLD MAN: Pardon?

QUEEN: Exactly.

OLD MAN: No, I mean 'I beg your pardon'.

QUEEN: And I grant it.

OLD MAN: No!

QUEEN: Yes! How many more times!

OLD MAN: But you can't pardon us.

QUEEN: I can! I do!

OLD MAN: We haven't done anything.

[*Short pause.*]

QUEEN: Pardon?

OLD MAN: Granted. I mean, we've done nothing to pardon. We came because of Giant Gormless.

[*Immediately all* THE GORMS *scream and scatter. They quiver with fear.*]

QUEEN: G-G-Giant Gormless? Aaaaaah!

[*In spite of her hot-water bottle, she slides terrified to the floor.*]

Do you work for him? Are you his spies? He's a cruel-hearted villain.

[THE LOCH-HAGGIS *have stepped out of their restraining hoops and try to comfort the quaking* GORMS.]

OLD MAN: No, no, certainly not.

QUEEN: Since he started ... [*with an effort*] ... Gorm-hunting...

[THE GORMS *twitter.*]

... we have been grotto-bound. Our heathercraft are grounded. Our food stores are empty. The Gorm Games have been cancelled.

OLD MAN: I know, your Gormness. The mysterious lack of purple heather gave me the clue. Then Giant Gorm-less ...

[THE GORMS *scream.*]

... paid me a visit.

QUEEN: And you escaped the clutches of such a giant? You are a miracle-worker.

OLD MAN: Well, I was bigger then, but that's another story. My Haggis and I are here to help you.

QUEEN: A champion! We have a champion!

[THE GORMS *cheer and start to return.*]

[*Suddenly, echoing footsteps from outside, followed by a booming voice, make everyone freeze.*]

Song Nine 'a': **Gorm Call (Fee, Fi)** (*reprise*)

GIANT GORMLESS: [*amplified voice from outside the grotto*]
Fee, fi, fo, fum
Gorms get ready, here I come!
Fee, fi ...
Aha!

[*Loud rustle of paper.*]

OLD MAN: [*whispers*] My map!

GIANT GORMLESS: [*voice-over*] What's this?

[*Sounds of kneeling down. Shadows move as* GIANT GORMLESS *blocks light from the grotto entrance.*]

Tiny writing.

QUEEN: Our signpost!

GIANT GORMLESS: [*voice-over*] Mm. Can't read it.

OLD MAN: Can't read. I knew he was stupid.

GIANT GORMLESS: [*voice-over*] Where's my telescope?

[*Noises of fumbling, then of a telescope being extended.*]

G-or-m G-r-ott-ohohoho!

QUEEN: He's not so stupid.

GIANT GORMLESS: [*voice-over*] Gorm Grotto! I've found it! I've found it! Hallo-o! Little Gor-ms! Can you hear me? Come out! I know you're there! You'd like to be famous, wouldn't you? Rich and famous? You could be the stars of my circus. See the world. Performing Gorms. Eh? Come out! Please!

> [*No response from* THE GORMS *except disapproval.*]

Mm. Need a bit of friendly persuasion do we?

> [*Suddenly* GIANT GORMLESS's *net (five times larger than when we first saw it) is pushed into the grotto through the offstage entrance.*]

> [THE GORMS *and* THE LOCH-HAGGIS *have to move fast to avoid the net.*]

Come on! Out you come!

> [*The net swings up and downstage as* GIANT GORMLESS *tries to catch* GORMS *in it.*]

> [*The net withdraws.*]

Ahh! Nothing, nothing! Try again.

> [*Back comes the net.*]

> [THE OLD MAN *takes charge.*]

OLD MAN: Gorms! Tug-o-war!

> [THE GORMS *understand and each takes a place along the handle of the net.*]

Take the strain!

GIANT GORMLESS: [*voice-over*] Ah! Caught something!

OLD MAN: Heave!

> [THE GORMS *heave.*]

GIANT GORMLESS: [*voice-over*] It's a big one!

OLD MAN: Heave!

> [*Struggling noises from* GIANT GORMLESS.]

Heave!

GIANT GORMLESS: [*voice-over*] Aaaaaah!

> [THE GORMS *pull the whole net into the cave.* THE LOCH-HAGGIS *cheer.*]

You little ... [*petulant*] You've taken my net!

> [THE OLD MAN *and* THE GORMS *congratulate each other.*]

It's the only one I've got! It's not fair!

> [THE GORMS *confidently stow away the net — against the grotto wall or offstage to another part of the grotto.*]

Thieving little Gorms! You'll pay for that! Where's my pipe?

OLD MAN: Pipe? What's he up to?

QUEEN: Maybe he's going to play us a tune?

[*Sound of a match striking and* GIANT GORM-LESS *sucking on a pipe.*]

[*Suddenly smoke is blown into the grotto.*]

OLD MAN: He's trying to smoke us out!

[*More smoke.*]

[*to* THE QUEEN] Do you have any fans?

QUEEN: Well, I like to think I'm quite popular...

OLD MAN: No, no, fans to fan away the smoke.

[THE GORMS *and* LOCH-HAGGIS *start coughing.*]

QUEEN: Alas, no.

OLD MAN: [*looking at* THE AUDIENCE] I wonder ... you've helped me before ... will you help the Gorms?

AUDIENCE: Yes!

QUEEN: You will?

AUDIENCE: Yes.

QUEEN: Thank you.

OLD MAN: Listen everybody. Blow! As hard as you can. Please. Blow the smoke away before we choke.

[THE AUDIENCE, *plus* GORMS *and* THE LOCH-HAGGIS *blow. The smoke retreats — eventually.*]

[*Sound of* GIANT GORMLESS *coughing violently.*]

[*to* THE AUDIENCE] You did it!

ALL: [*to* THE AUDIENCE] Thank you!

[*Silence from outside.*]

QUEEN: Has he gone?

[*All listen.*]

GIANT GORMLESS: [*voice-over: concerned*] Silly little Gorms. I didn't mean to hurt you. I want you fit and alive, not ... are you all right in there?

[*Pause.*]

[*grunting as he bends down*] Mm. Any sound of life?

[*Suddenly* GORM 1 *sees something — shadows form as the entrance is covered.*]

GORM 1: Look!

OLD MAN: Shhh!

GORM 2: [*whispers*] What's that?

GORM 3: A giant ear!

> [THE LOCH-HAGGIS *suddenly giggle and surround* THE OLD MAN.]

OLD MAN: Quiet!

> [*But* THE LOCH-HAGGIS *are insistent: they have an idea.*]

LOCH-HAGGIS 1: Make noises!

LOCH-HAGGIS 2: Loud noises!

LOCH-HAGGIS 3: In his ear!

GIANT GORMLESS: [*voice-over*] Ah! I can hear something.

OLD MAN: Good idea! [*to* THE AUDIENCE] Come on, everybody, attack! I know — bagpipe noises! The nastier the better. All together. After three! One, two, three!

> [*All encourage* THE AUDIENCE *to make deafening bagpipe noises.*]

> [*Eventually:*]

GIANT GORMLESS: [*voice-over*] Aaaaaah! No! No!

> [*The light from the entrance returns as* GIANT GORMLESS *moves his ear away from the noise. Footsteps running away.*]

OLD MAN: He's gone! Well done! Thank you.

> [*All cheer.*]

QUEEN: Thank you, sir, thank you.

OLD MAN: Thank the Haggis. It was their idea.

QUEEN: Indeed it was. You shall be rewarded. What would you like?

> [THE LOCH-HAGGIS *rub their stomachs.*]

LOCH-HAGGIS 1: Mm. Hungry.

LOCH-HAGGIS 2: Yummy, yummy, hungry.

LOCH-HAGGIS 3: Food, food, yummy, hungry.

QUEEN: I'm sorry. No can do. [*to* THE OLD MAN] As I said, our food stores are empty. Sorry, Haggis.

OLD MAN: Don't worry, ma'am. They're always hungry.

> [*They are interrupted by echoing footsteps. All freeze again.*]

Suffering sporrans, the Sassenach's back!

QUEEN: Hasn't he suffered enough?

OLD MAN: Some giants never learn.

GIANT GORMLESS: [*voice-over*] Hallo-o! Gorms! I know when I'm beaten. And you've beaten me fair and square. If you don't want to be the world-famous Performing Gorms, that's fair enough with me.

[*All smile, temporarily taken in by his soft-soap approach.*]

But let me leave you as your friend, not your enemy. Here you are! A peace offering.

[*Into the grotto slides a large oatcake spiked by a stick.* THE GORMS *examine it.*]

GORM 1: What is it?

GORM 2: Smells good.

GORM 3: Tastes good too, I bet.

GORM 4: It's an oatcake.

GORM 5: Come on ...

GORM 6: Lunch-time!

[*They go to eat.*]

OLD MAN: Stop! Don't touch it. I don't trust him.

QUEEN: Looks harmless enough.

GIANT GORMLESS: [*voice-over*] Have you got it? Don't be shy!

OLD MAN: It may be a trick. Leave it.

[*Reluctantly* THE GORMS *back away from the oatcake.*]

[*Suddenly* THE LOCH-HAGGIS *rush forward, unable to resist.*]

LOCH-HAGGIS: Mm! Yummy yummy! Tasty tasty! Food! Food! [*etc.*]

[*As they grab the oatcake, it is pulled back towards the entrance.*]

OLD MAN: No! Aggie! Maggie! Hamish!

[*But the* LOCH-HAGGIS *follow the oatcake out of the grotto.*]

Come back, you stupid Haggis!

GIANT GORMLESS: [*voice-over*] Gotcha! Gotcha! Gotcha!

[*Giggly shrieks from* THE LOCH-HAGGIS.]

Ha, ha, ha! Hallo, Gorms. That's it, tuck in! I'll take good care of you, wait and see!

[*Happy sounds of* THE LOCH-HAGGIS *eating. Giant footsteps retreating. Then silence.*]

QUEEN: He thinks the Haggis are Gorms.

OLD MAN: I told you he was stupid. Almost as stupid as the Haggis. They'll be very happy together, I'm sure.

QUEEN: You don't mind losing them?

OLD MAN: To be honest, I never wanted them in the first place. And if they lived with me they'd eat me out of cave and home. Giant Gormless is bound to keep them well fed — otherwise they won't perform for him.

QUEEN: Then all's well that ends well.

OLD MAN: Let's hope so, ma'am.

QUEEN: We must celebrate.

OLD MAN: I must go.

QUEEN: You must be our Guest of Honour!

[THE GORMS *cheer and carry* THE OLD MAN *to the throne and seat him on it.*]

Song Ten: **The Gorm Games**

The Gorm Games are cancelled
Is cancelled!
By which I mean to say
That I'm cancelling the cancellation
So the Gorm Games take place today
Let the Gorm Games get under way!

[*The 'Cancelled' notices are removed from the 'Gorm Games' posters.*]

[*To music, various games are played, linked by* GORM *acrobatics, and introduced by* THE QUEEN*: 'Bursting the Bagpipe' (like a balloon); 'Scotch Hop'; 'Knife and Fork Dance' (like a sword dance); 'Throwing the Hammer' (a giant hammer); 'Spider's Footsteps' (like Grandmother's Footsteps); 'Lifting the Lolly' (two lollipops lashed together as dumbbells); 'Tossing the Pancake'; 'Jumping the Thistle'.*]

[*Then ...*]

And finally, to express our thanks to our friend, the Old Man of Lochnagar, who saved the Gorm

Kingdom from Giant Gormless, we decorate him with the highest Gorm honour — the Order of the Gorm Thistle.

[*Applause as* THE OLD MAN *is given his thistle medal.*]

OLD MAN: Thank you, ma'am. I'm happy to have been of service. And now I really must be getting home.

[*He is helped off the throne.*]

But I have a wee problem. Lagopus Scoticus gave me a potion to make me grow smaller, but nothing to make me grow bigger again.

QUEEN: Fear not! Listen ...

Song Eleven: **Drink and Grow**

Drink a dram of Stag Beetle's milk
Rich and creamy and smooth as silk
Soon you'll find to your surprise
Back you'll grow to normal size!

OLD MAN: Stag Beetle's milk? But where do I find that?
QUEEN: In a Stag Beetle! Where else!

[*Fanfare.* THE GORMS *step aside as* A STAG BEETLE *enters and takes* THE OLD MAN *by surprise.*]

[*Music as* THE OLD MAN *chases and catches* THE STAG BEETLE *and, with difficulty, milks it.* THE GORMS *cheer him on and provide a jug for the milk.*]

Song (continued)

[*as* THE OLD MAN *drinks*]

ALL: Drink a dram of Stag Beetle's milk
Rich and creamy and smooth as silk
Soon you'll find to your surprise
Back you'll grow to normal size!

[THE OLD MAN *drinks. The lighting flickers magically. Sound effects.*]

OLD MAN: [*still holding the jug*] Thank you. It's working!

QUEEN: You must hurry, otherwise you'll never get out!

OLD MAN: Farewell!

QUEEN: Farewell!

ALL: Farewell!

> [THE OLD MAN *goes. At the last moment* A
> GORM *hands him his overnight bag.*]

QUEEN: Now, Gorms, normal duties are resumed. Heather-spraying tonight. Prepare for squirt-off!

> [*Music as the thistle-treading barrel is brought in.*]

Song Twelve: **Tread the Thistle**

GORMS: We
Whistle
As we tread the thistle
(Whistle)
Squeeze the
Juice from ev'ry bristle
(Whistle)
Stamp, stamp
Tramp, tramp, tramp
Stomp, stomp
Clomp, clomp, clomp
We
Whistle
As we tread the thistle
(Whistle)
Squeeze the
Juice from ev'ry bristle
(Whistle).

> [*To music,* THE GORMS *perform the traditional
> 'Treading the Thistle' choreographed routine.*]

We
Whistle
As we tread the thistle
(Whistle)
Squeeze the
Juice from ev'ry bristle
(Whistle)

Stamp, stamp
Tramp, tramp, tramp
Stomp, stomp
Clomp, clomp, clomp
We
Whistle
As we tread the thistle
(Whistle)
Squeeze the
Juice from ev'ry bristle
(Whistle).

> [*As the song ends, music continues as a tube and nozzle (like those of a petrol pump) are attached to the barrel.*]

> [*Then, with a fanfare, enter the heathercraft itself,* A GORM *at the controls.* GORMS *begin to fill its tank with thistle dye.*]

> [*Blackout.*]

SCENE FOUR — The Entrance to Gorm Grotto

Normal size, as at the beginning of Act Two, Scene One.

GIANT GORMLESS *is playing with* THE LOCH-HAGGIS *(puppet-size). He himself operates one, which is 'standing' in his specimen box. The other two are on the rock.*

Lighting isolates GIANT GORMLESS *and* THE PUPPET-LOCH-HAGGIS.

Song Twelve 'a': **Gathering Gorms** (*reprise*)

GIANT GORMLESS: Ha ha! Hee hee! Ho ho ho!
Ha ha! Hee hee! Ho ho ho!

You great little physical jerkers
Will love being my little workers
I'll teach you some tricks
Somersaults and high kicks
And you can perform in my circus.

Gorms, Gorms
My dream has come true now
Gorms, Gorms
Today I've found you, how
Happy I'm feeling
My wheeling and dealing
Means now I'm not gormless no more!

Ha ha! Hee hee! Ho ho ho!

I've proved
I'm no ignoramus
Gorms will
Make me rich and famous
Honoured, respected
No longer neglected
I'll never be gormless again!
Ho ho ho!

[*Lighting increases to include the entrance to Gorm Grotto. Enter, with difficulty,* THE OLD MAN, *just squeezing through the small entrance to Gorm Grotto.*]

OLD MAN: Just made it!
[*He sees* GIANT GORMLESS.]
Hallo. Good hunting?

GIANT GORMLESS: I'll say so. Look at my lovely little Gorms. [*to* THE PUPPET-LOCH-HAGGIS] Wave to the Old Man, like good Gorms.
[THE PUPPET-LOCH-HAGGIS *wave.*]
See that!

OLD MAN: Yes! Hallo, Gorms! They're very well-behaved.

GIANT GORMLESS: Of course. I'm training them. For my circus. [*to* THE PUPPET-LOCH-HAGGIS] You're looking forward to the circus, aren't you, Gorms?
[THE PUPPET-LOCH-HAGGIS *nod and squeak.*]
Yes! [*confidentially*] My only disappointment is their size. Their lack of stature.

OLD MAN: Really?

GIANT GORMLESS: I had hoped for more developed Gorms. Maybe they'll grow. [*to* THE PUPPET-LOCH-HAGGIS] More oatcake, Gorms? [*to* THE OLD MAN] Food's good for growth.

[THE OLD MAN *notices he is still carrying the jug — very small now — of* STAG BEETLE'*s milk.*]

OLD MAN: I — er ... think I might be able to help you there.

GIANT GORMLESS: Where?

OLD MAN: Here. And now. Allow me.

Song Twelve 'b': **Drink and Grow** (*reprise*)

[THE OLD MAN *gives each* PUPPET-LOCH-HAGGIS *a drink from the jug.*]

Drink a dram of Stag Beetle's milk
Rich and creamy and smooth as silk
Soon you'll find to your surprise
Back you'll grow to normal size!

[*The lighting flickers. Sound effects.*]

[THE PUPPET-LOCH-HAGGIS *disappear and the normal-sized (actor)* LOCH-HAGGIS *appear. They giggle and affectionately nuzzle against* GIANT GORMLESS.]

GIANT GORMLESS: Hey! It's magic! Thank you! Thank you, Old Man! Hallo, Gorms! Are you hungry? Stop tickling. Come along!

[*As they leave, it is clear that* GIANT GORMLESS *has quite a handful.*]

OLD MAN: Farewell, Giant Gormless.

GIANT GORMLESS: [*turning*] Oh no! I'm not Gormless any more!

[THE LOCH-HAGGIS *giggle and wave.*]

Bye.

[THE LOCH-HAGGIS *and* GIANT GORMLESS *exit.*]

OLD MAN: Little does he know! He's as gormless as ever! The Gorms are safe — [*to* THE AUDIENCE] — thanks to you and me! And he'll never know — as long as we all keep the secret! Now, home. [*seeing his map, in the heather*] Hey! He's forgotten my map. How considerate!

[*He sets off, looks back at the entrance to Gorm Grotto, and returns. He bends down and calls in.*]

All clear, Gorms! Heathercraft chocks away!

[*As he walks off, fade to:*]

[*Blackout.*]

SCENE FIVE — The Sky

Song Thirteen: **Purpling the Heather**
(Heather Lament — *reprise*)

QUEEN: [*voice-over*]
Fly to the heather
The white heather
Cover the heather
With purple spray
Turn the white heather
To purple heather
Chocks away!

[*Sound effects of the heathercraft take-off.*]

[*A shadow puppet sequence or a U.V. sequence against black.*]

[*A heathercraft appears, small — as though in the distance. Its silhouette is seen against the rising moon. It exits.*]

[*Another — larger — heathercraft enters, crosses and exits.*]

[*Moonlight shines on the heather in the fore-ground. It is white.*]

[*The heathercraft appears (even larger), and sprays down the purple thistle dye.*]

[*The heather dramatically turns purple and, as the music reaches its climax, the auditorium turns purple!*]

[*Blackout.*]

SCENE SIX — The Old Man's Cave

THE OLD MAN *sits in his chair, snoring and whistling, in exactly the same position as when he fell asleep in Act One, Scene One.*

Gradually the lighting brightens as though morning has risen.

Suddenly the deerskin door is drawn aside and in bustles GROUSE, *carrying a basket of goodies.*

She registers the sleeping OLD MAN *with impatience, then lights the stove. She takes a large cooking pot, goes to fill it from a jar marked 'Heather Porridge', thinks better of it, picks up a wooden spoon, creeps to a position inches from* THE OLD MAN's *ear, then bangs the spoon loudly against the cooking pot.*

THE OLD MAN *wakes with a jump.*

OLD MAN: Oh, 'tis you, Grouse.

GROUSE: Aye, 'tis I, Old Man.
[*She returns to the stove and starts preparing heather porridge.*]

OLD MAN: Good morning.

GROUSE: Huh! Little good about *my* morning. I've been off my nest since dawn flying hither and thither on your behalf. My wings are dropping off.

OLD MAN: Oh, stop grousing, Grousy.

GROUSE: 'Tis all very well for you. Snoring your selfish old head off till I arrive with your breakfast.

OLD MAN: Ah. Breakfast!
[*He sits at the table.*]
You're a jewel, Grousy. A wee gem! A treasure!

GROUSE: You're just saying that.

OLD MAN: Because it's true.

GROUSE: Because you want your breakfast.

OLD MAN: Well, I wouldna say no. What is there?

GROUSE: Heather porridge with fresh clover juice.

OLD MAN: Delicious!

GROUSE: [*producing them from her bag*] Newly picked blaeberries.

OLD MAN: Blaeberries! My favourite fruit!

GROUSE: Three slices of deer bacon.

OLD MAN: Mm! Deer bacon, you dear Grouse!

GROUSE: And ... though ...

OLD MAN: [*suddenly, as though remembering*] ... why I bother, heaven alone knows ... a ptarmigan's egg.

GROUSE: [*surprised*] Aye. How did you know that?

OLD MAN: I ... I'm not sure. I'd heard it before ... I ... it's all coming back ... and ... and you've brought something else, haven't you? Something to brighten up the cave ...

GROUSE: Aye, some ...

OLD MAN: Don't tell me! [*hesitantly*] Some heather.

[GROUSE *nods, mystified by* THE OLD MAN'*s behaviour.*]

What colour heather?

GROUSE: What colour? What a question! Purple, of course.

[*She produces it.*]

OLD MAN: [*relieved, but maybe a little disappointed*] My favourite!

GROUSE: Heaven help me if I brought you white. You'd be grumbling away at me all day, you fussy Old Man.

[*She brings him his heather porridge.*]

OLD MAN: Then I must have ... it was all a ...

GROUSE: Stop your chuntering and eat your porridge while it's hot. You look as though you've seen a Gorm!

OLD MAN: Maybe I have, Grousy.

[*He remembers something and feels in his pocket. Slowly he brings out the Order of the Gorm Thistle.*]

Maybe I have.

[*He smiles in triumph, sharing his secret with* THE AUDIENCE.]

THE END